NICOLAS COPERNICVS

MCCCLXIV — MCD

THE FRONTISPIECE DESIGN AND ITS SYMBOLISM

THE ARTIST

The frontispiece design was contributed by a refugee Polish artist, Arthur Szyk, perhaps the greatest living miniaturist working in the technique of illuminated medieval manuscripts. Although Mr. Szyk is best known to the American public through his striking caricatures of the leading characters of the so-called "New Order in Europe," yet among his best works have been those in which he portrayed some of the outstanding personalities in Polish and American history. His inimitable style and technique found an excellent expression in this portrayal of Copernicus, as no other artist could depict so many symbols within so few inches of space with so much meaning.

THE SYMBOLISM

Copernicus is represented here as a churchman and a scholar—more specifically, as astronomer. The chain and cap (with the Jagiellonian white eagle) are academic symbols. In the left hand he holds a device which illustrates one of his astronomical principles of planetary motions, with the sun in the center. In front of him is an enlarged fragment of the Jagiellonian golden globe (see photographic reproduction of the original globe within).

In the upper left-hand corner is Wawel, the Polish Acropolis, with the center of Kraków as it looked in his student days (1491-95). In the upper right-hand corner is the coat-of-arms of the University of Kraków (*Universitas Cracoviensis*). The Roman numerals (1364-1400) indicate the years when the university was founded and renovated, respectively. On the table are the Holy Bible and the inkwell. Red and white are Polish national colors. The various texts speak for themselves—and their import is also made clear within this monograph. The lantern is such as he used on his observation tower at night.

Within the border design are:

At the bottom, the Polish white eagle of the Jagiellonian period.

In the left, coat-of-arms of Gniezno, the first capital of Poland.

In the right, coat-of-arms of Kraków, the capital of Poland in his student days.

At the top, coat-of-arms of his native city Torun.

NICHOLAS COPERNICUS

178469

NICHOLAS COPERNICUS

1543 - 1943

By STEPHEN P. MIZWA, A.M., LL.D.

THE KOSCIUSZKO FOUNDATION
NEW YORK

1943

PREFACE

THE AUTHOR IS, of course, fully conscious of the effort that he himself has contributed in the preparation of this booklet so that it would not offend the eye and yet retain some value — besides that of a mere souvenir — after it has served its present purpose. As measured by the demands of the subject and the occasion, he is also painfully aware that the result, such as it is, does not do full justice to the subject and may not completely fulfill the expectation of the occasion.

But the shortcomings would have been even greater, and certainly much more numerous, had it not been for the timely assistance of those to whom the author desires to express his gratitude. Thus, in the first place, to Dr. Henry Noble MacCracken, President of Vassar College and of the Kosciuszko Foundation, for having read the entire manuscript and for his encouragement and friendly advice. Secondly, to Dr. Oscar Halecki, the outstanding contemporary Polish historian, Professor of History at the University of Warsaw and now Director of the Polish Institute of Arts and Sciences in New York, for his careful scrutiny of the historical angles of this monograph. The outline map of Poland in the days of Copernicus was also prepared under his supervision. And no less to Dr. Edward Rosen of the City College of New York — our own leading Copernican scholar — for his perusal of the scientific phases and bibliographical suggestions and for his many helpful comments.

As a result of this triple revision, many an ambiguous word or phrase has been caught and eliminated, thereby giving the author a certain degree of courage to feel that the story he has told has gained a measure of reliability that could not otherwise have been achieved.

S. P. M.

CONTENTS

Page

PART I. THE LIFE-STORY OF COPERNICUS

Copernicus the Astronomer 11
Copernicus the Economist 15
Churchman, Statesman and Soldier—A Biographical Sketch 16
Slow Recognition of the New Truth 22
The Death of Copernicus and the Birth of Modern Science 24

PART II. *SARMATICUS ASTRONOMUS*

The Cradle of the Family: Silesia and Krakow 34
The Name Kopernik and Its Meaning 36
"On the Mother's Side" 37
"Prussian Poland," Torun and Varmia 40
"Writing on the Wall" and Other Mementos 41
Medals 48
Public Monuments 49
Why Are the Poles Proud of Copernicus? 54
A Voice from England Across the Century 55
Footnote References 57
Bibliographical Suggestions and Comments 60

PART III. PROGRAM SUGGESTIONS

Program Suggestions 65
I.   Short Program 66
II. The Copernican Quadricentennial Program 67
Explanations (of program items) 68
The Copernican Quadricentennial National Committee 72
Music and Costumes 73-78

PART IV. IN THE NAME OF COPERNICUS

Is Poland to be a "Cultural Wilderness"? 79
Best American Books as Nucleus 81
Two Chairs in American Civilization 83

THE KOSCIUSZKO FOUNDATION 86

MISCELLANEA 88

THE COPERNICAN SOLAR SYSTEM

The plate on the reverse page illustrates the solar system as conceived by Copernicus in his great book *De Revolutionibus Orbium Coelestium*. The sun is in the center. The inside circle, nearest to the sun, carries the planet Mercury; next to it is the orbit of Venus; and then comes that of the earth around which, in turn, revolves the moon. The larger circles outside the earth represent the motions of Mars, Jupiter and Saturn respectively. Those are the primary planets which could be observed by the naked eye and were known to Copernicus. The last and largest circle stands for the immobile sphere of the fixed stars.

New planets were later successively discovered by other astronomers with the aid of a telescope. Thus, Sir William Herschel discovered Uranus in 1781. In 1846 a young student at Cambridge University, John C. Adams, discovered Neptune.

Mean distances from the sun to the various planets mentioned above were computed later on and are as follows:

Mercury	36,000,000 miles
Venus	67,200,000 miles
Earth	92,900,000 miles
Mars	141,500,000 miles
Jupiter	483,300,000 miles
Saturn	886,100,000 miles
Uranus	1,782,800,000 miles
Neptune	2,793,500,000 miles

THE COPERNICAN
SOLAR SYSTEM

*I*t has always seemed to me that the real significance of the heliocentric system lies in the greatness of this conception rather than in the fact of the discovery itself. There is no figure in astronomical history which may more appropriately claim the admiration of mankind through all time than that of Copernicus.

Simon Newcomb[1]

NICHOLAS COPERNICUS

(From steel engraving by E. de Boulanois, Brussels, 1682)

Part I

THE LIFE-STORY OF COPERNICUS

IKOLAJ KOPERNIK, best known by his Latinized name of Nicolaus[2]* Copernicus, was the most original and not the least versatile genius of Poland. He was a churchman, a painter and a poet, a physician, an economist, a statesman, a soldier, and a scientist; a churchman by the wish of his guardian uncle and by vocation, an artist for relaxation, a physician by training and predilection, an economist by accident, a statesman and a soldier by necessity, and a scientist — by the Grace of God and by sheer love of the truth for truth's sake. "Yet he found time," says the English historian of astronomy, A. M. Clerke, "to elaborate an entirely new system of astronomy, by the adoption of which man's outlook on the universe was fundamentally changed."

And today,—when for the first time in 575 years the Alma Mater of Copernicus has been closed by the invader, when the intellectual leadership of the nation is being extirpated and all visible monuments of Polish civilization destroyed,— today Copernicus stands like a shining star of hope to the nation that nurtured him, and the recollection of his abiding contribution gives his compatriots courage to endure.

COPERNICUS THE ASTRONOMER

Stripped of all scientific verbiage and reduced to the simplest elements, Copernicus's contribution in the field of astronomy

---

*All footnote references on pp. 57-59.

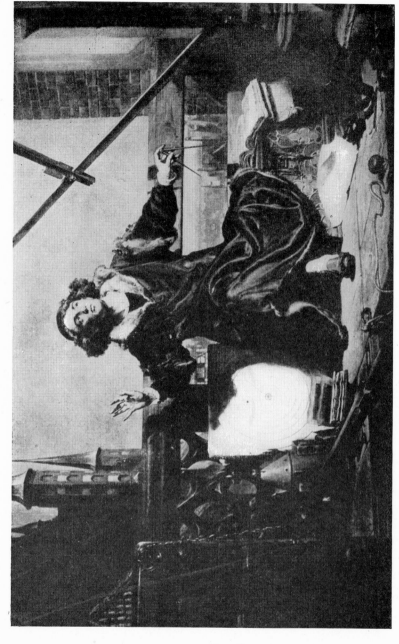

Nicholas Copernicus on the observation tower at the Cathedral of Frauenberg, by Jan Matejko (1838-93), the Polish national painter. The original oil painting was hanging till September, 1939, in the main assembly hall of the University of Krakow.

may be stated in the words: "He stopped the sun and set the earth in motion."

From time immemorial, ever since man began to peep through the crevice of his cave and noted the wonders of the heavens, the sun and moon and stars and their comings and goings, the behavior of celestial bodies had always been a mystery. Sages of the ages tried to adduce causes that would explain these phenomena perceived by the senses. Finally the Greek geographer and astronomer Ptolemy, who lived in Alexandria in the second century of our era, and who systematized the ideas and elaborations of all his predecessors, promulgated a system that was maintained and met no successful challenge for fourteen centuries.

It was a system based on the testimony of the senses, the geocentric conception, that supposed the earth to be the fixed center of the universe about which the sun and the other six planets revolve. That's what appeared to the eyesight as the sun rose and set and apparently moved round the earth, as the moon and other planets of the solar system changed their positions with respect to the earth.

It was the Ptolemaic geocentric system which prevailed until Copernicus bade the sun to stop, and at his bidding the earth began to spin. Contrary to the testimony of the senses, Copernicus completely reversed the system by superseding it with the heliocentric conception. In this new Copernican system the sun was the center round which moved the earth, the moon and other planets. Thanks to Copernicus and to his great work *De Revolutionibus Orbium Coelestium* (literally, "Concerning the Revolutions of the Heavenly Spheres") — the first copy of which its creator beheld with dimmed eyes on his deathbed—humanity got the key to the riddle which had been puzzling and troubling it for many thousands of years.

[13]

Copernicus explains his De Monetae Cudendae Ratio (Concerning the Principle of Coining Money) at a session of the provincial diet in Grudziadz, 1522.

By superseding the Ptolemaic geocentric system with his own, Copernicus, with his daring and fantastic imagination, gave us a new conception of this puny, tiny little vale of tears of ours we call the world and a new magnificent vista of the heavens above us and the universe around us. Even God and man assumed new meanings. The conception of distances could be transferred from the criteria of walking-time to those of millions of light years. Following the Copernican conception, it was discovered later that in our own solar neighborhood the earth is ninety-three millions of miles from the sun; Mars over one hundred and forty millions of miles; and Saturn over eight hundred eighty-six millions of miles. And those are only the nearest neighborly planets of our own solar system. Beyond this, there are millions of other solar systems, millions of light years away from ours. To use Copernicus's own words: "So large indeed is the divine workshop of the Almighty."

COPERNICUS THE ECONOMIST

Copernicus the astronomer also made an important contribution to our knowledge of the monetary law, for which Sir Thomas Gresham (1519-79) got the credit in economic literature through an error made by the Scottish economist H. D. Macleod. In 1857 Macleod suggested the name of Gresham's Law as he was under the impression that the principle was first explained by Thomas Gresham in 1558.

Gresham's Law in economics—in brief, the principle that when bad money is in circulation with the good, the bad regulates the value of all and drives out the good—might also be called Copernicus's Law. For it was Copernicus who first formulated this principle with clarity in 1526 in his treatise *De Monetae Cudendae Ratio* (Concerning the Principle of Coining Money), 32 years before the promulgation of this monetary law by Gresham. To be sure, there was a Frenchman in the XIV century named Nicole Oresme, who established a sound coinage for King Charles V (in 1355-58) and adumbrated Gresham's Law, but as Macleod himself later explained: "Copernicus wrote his treatise entirely without the knowledge of the preceding one of Oresme." And he spoke of Copernicus as "the founder of modern astronomy and one of the founders of a most important branch of economics."

It is not impossible that Copernicus might have known of Oresme's treatise, but the astronomer-economist formulated his law of bad money with a scientific precision not evident in any of his predecessors. Curiously, though a churchman, he attacked the problem not from the moral but from the realistic and social angles. Debasing the coinage was not a sin but bad economic practice which always brings about disastrous social consequences—in terms of rising prices. He did not use the word *inflation*, but realized its meaning and described its consequences. Debasing of the coinage, in his opinion, was one of four disasters that could befall a nation; the other three being discord, high mortality and poor harvests.

CHURCHMAN, STATESMAN AND SOLDIER
A BIOGRAPHICAL SKETCH

Nicholas Copernicus came of an old Silesian family. One of its branches moved (about 1350) to Krakow and in time became wealthy merchants in that ancient capital of Poland. When in 1454 the Union of Pomeranian territories and towns together with Danzig and Torun revolted against the Teutonic Order and asked the Polish king to take them back under the sovereignty of Poland, Nicholas Copernicus the Elder moved to Torun (about 1458) and it was here that the famous astronomer was born on February 19, 1473.

He spent his childhood in Torun and attended the Parochial School at St. John's Church. When his father died in

1483, he was put under the guardianship of his maternal uncle, later bishop and Polish Senator, Lucas Watzelrod, under whose tutelage he prepared himself for higher studies most probably in the Cathedral School of nearby Wloclawek. From 1491 to 1495 he studied at the ancient Polish University of Krakow.[3] Very little information has been preserved about the student days of Copernicus in this university—or in any university for that matter. Historians of astronomy are generally agreed, however, that while at Krakow he studied or came under the spell of that brilliant Polish astronomer and mathematician, Albert Brudzewski, or Wojciech z Brudzewa (1445-1495) as he is sometimes called, who was undoubtedly the first to inspire the young pupil in astronomy with the beauty of this old science. The first thrill that came to Copernicus from the handling of astronomical instruments and

View of Krakow in 1493, in the student days of Copernicus. In the center background is the Wawel (castle and cathedral), the Polish Acropolis; in the center, with two towers, is the famous St. Mary's Church, "from one of whose towers a trumpeter plays . . . the hejnal *every hour on the hour of day and of night"; to the left, across the river Vistula, is Kazimierz* (Casimirus), *a suburb which grew into a Jewish community. The location of the university is indicated by the circle.*

[17]

BRUDZEWSKI PROFESOR COPERNICI

ALBERT BRUDZEWSKI

*"the first great teacher of the
great astronomer."*

observation of the heavens was experienced in this "city of living stones".[4]

We happen to know that in September of 1494, i.e. during the last year of Copernicus's student days in Krakow, there were brought from Buda, Hungary, as gifts of Marcin Bylica[5] to the University of Krakow, four astronomical instruments. Primitive from our point of view but the last word in scientific equipment in those days, they were: a large celestial globe, two beautiful astrolabes and a *triquetrum*. The arrival of these instruments created such a sensation, we are told by documented histories of the university, that the Rector called a special student assembly to behold and admire these wonders. They have been preserved at the University of Krakow to this day. There is no doubt but that Copernicus was one of the most interested spectators.

We know much more about the first great teacher of the great astronomer. Albert Brudzewski, who was also a teacher of Bernard Wapowski (a life-long friend of Copernicus and an eminent Polish historian), was one of the most active exponents of Humanism in Krakow. Although he taught the Ptolemaic system, he was a man of liberal sympathies and a "born teacher." He knew how to arouse his students' interests and encourage independent thinking. The discussions he provoked were often carried to the street, not infrequently ending in fist fights among students holding rival opinions.

For further study Copernicus went to Italy. At his uncle's request he enrolled as a student of canon law at Bologna University, but did not give up his scientific studies. Here he came in contact with the unorthodox astronomer Domenico Maria Novara (1454-1504). Although, thanks to his uncle's influence, he was elected a Canon[6] of Varmia (Ermland)—which gave him an independent income—Copernicus remained in Bologna to

While in Rome (in 1500), Copernicus observing an eclipse of the moon. From Louis Figuier, Vies Des Savants, *Paris, 1881.*

continue his studies and possibly astronomical observations. In the year 1500 he went to Rome, where he also lectured on mathematics and astronomy. While in Rome he observed an eclipse of the moon. From 1501 to 1503 he studied medicine at the University of Padua and at the same time obtained a doctor's degree in canon law at Ferrara.

From 1504 or 1505 on he assumed his active duties as canon of the duchy-bishopric of Varmia, acted as physician and personal secretary to his uncle, Bishop Lucas, devoted much time to healing of the poor, continued his astronomical observations and took active part in political events of the day as the most inveterate enemy of the so-called Knights of the Teutonic Order, then headed by Albert of Hohenzollern (1490-1568), the last grand master of the Order. The latter was trying to create internal dissensions and foment disorders in the Polish provinces, especially in Varmia, which was surrounded by the

The famous "Jagiellonian golden globe," constructed about 1510, in the collection of the University of Krakow library. The first globe constructed on the Copernican theory of the motion of the earth, moved by a clock mechanism, on which the newly discovered American continent was placed with the legend: America terra noviter reperta *(America, the newly discovered land). An enlarged fragment of this globe is reproduced by Mr. Szyk in the cover design.*

Teutonic possessions on three sides.[7] When war with the Teutonic Order broke out in 1520, Copernicus the churchman, physician and astronomer, became commander in chief of his beleaguered city of Olsztyn (Allenstein). Soon after that, at the request of Sigismund I, King of Poland, he took active part in the currency reforms of Varmia and neighboring provinces.

It was at this post as administrator of church property of the duchy-bishopric of Varmia, not infrequently interrupted by political activities and armed conflicts, that Nicholas Copernicus labored, observed and tabulated his data the rest of his active life—culminating in *De Revolutionibus*—and it was here that after exhaustion, paralyzed, deprived of memory and consciousness, he passed on to his eternal reward on May 24, 1543.

"De Revolutionibus Orbium Coelestium—*The first copy of which its creator beheld with his dimmed eyes on his deathbed.*"

Illustration from Louis Figuier, Vies Des Savants, *Paris, 1881.*

"His theory," says Dr. Dorothy Stimson in her scholarly study *The Gradual Acceptance of the Copernican Theory of the Universe,* "is a triumph of reason and imagination and with its almost complete independence of authority is perhaps as original a work as an human being may be expected to produce."

Yet in spite of this, or rather because of it, the very publication of Copernicus's *De Revolutionibus* was a tragedy in itself; and after publication, the new truth had to struggle for recognition and acceptance for over two hundred years.

Audacious as a thinker and not lacking even in physical courage, Copernicus was timid in pushing his own discoveries. He wanted to work out, check and recheck, all details before eventual publication. "When therefore I had pondered these matters," he explained later in his dedication, "the scorn which was to be feared on account of the novelty and the absurdity of the opinion impelled me for that reason to set aside entirely the book already drawn up." The testimony of the senses was against him and he was also afraid that the Church, of which he was a faithful son, might take exception to his revolutionary theory.

Finally, when he was persuaded by a young astronomer and disciple of his, George Joachim Rheticus of Wittenberg, to have his priceless manuscript published in Nuremberg, the proofreading was unfortunately entrusted to Andreas Osiander, who was not worthy of the confidence placed in him. In order to mollify possible opposition of the Church and perhaps enlist its support in the promulgation of the new truth, Copernicus wrote a splendid dedicatory letter to Pope Paul III intended as a preface to *De Revolutionibus*. Having previously failed to persuade Copernicus to write an introduction explaining that the new system is merely a hypothesis, useful for calculations but not necessarily true, Osiander now took advantage of Copernicus's illness and anonymously inserted a foreword of his own, at the same time suppressing the author's introduction to Book I. Fortunately Copernicus was spared the agony caused by betrayal as his dim eyesight did not catch this anonymous foreword. For years it was thought that it was Copernicus who wrote this "Osiandric" foreword in order to disarm criticism. Perhaps, unwittingly, Osiander rendered a much greater service than he realized for the preservation of this great work. Because of this spurious and disarming foreword, cleverly addressed, as though in the name of the author, "to the reader of the hypotheses of this work" *(ad lectorem de hypothesibus huius operis),* the Church overlooked the revolutionary importance of *De Revolutionibus* and did not put it on the Index till 1616. It remained on the Index until 1835.

In the Protestant countries the general acceptance of the Copernican theory was somewhat accelerated but not too perceptibly. It should however be observed here, to the credit of his Church, that although it was slower in accepting the Copernican system as established scientific truth, it neither persecuted its creator nor exposed him to ridicule. This much cannot be said of the contemporary religious reformers, who were less tolerant. Martin Luther (1483-1546) referred to Copernicus as the "new astrologer," concerning whose contribution his judgment was: "The fool will overturn the whole system of astronomy."[8] Indeed he did. It took one hundred and fifty years for *De Revolutionibus* to be approved by European scholars and mathematicians; another generation more before the Copernican system was openly taught at Oxford, Sorbonne and at Yale; and two generations after that before the common people were ready for this revolutionary conception.

It is worthy of note that in our Colonial America, as early

as 1721 Cotton Mather conceded that the "Copernican hypothesis is now generally preferred," and that "there is no objection against the motion of the earth."

THE DEATH OF COPERNICUS—AND THE BIRTH OF MODERN SCIENCE

Copernicus lived, worked and died in that period which is generally regarded as a transition from the so-called middle ages to modern times. It was a period of the revival of learning and of the birth of modern science.

In art and literature there was recovery of classical culture and its revitalization and adaptation to Christian civilization. In the relationships of groups of men this period saw the dawn of modern nationalities, although only a bare adumbration of the dawn, as well as the birth of modern languages. The restless spirits launched upon exploration of the unknown and discovery of new continents.

In science especially there was a change of outlook and of manner of approach in quest of new truths; a change from meditation to experimentation. Men began to question that which was handed down to them as unquestionable and commenced to find out for themselves—not through excogitation but through observation, by objective standards, by weighing and measuring. It was in this transitional era that the Copernican system of astronomy was inaugurated and finally replaced the Ptolemaic system.

Leonardo da Vinci (1452-1519), the great Italian painter and natural philosopher, who constantly poked around trying to discover the hidden laws of nature, was a contemporary of Copernicus; his immediate successors were the celebrated English experimental philosopher, Francis Bacon (1561-1626), and Galileo (1564-1642), another great Italian, astronomer and physicist. Equipped with the newly invented telescope (generally accepted as in Holland, 1608), which he improved, Galileo carried on astronomical observations where Copernicus left off.

Tycho Brahe (1546-1601), the Danish astronomer, who was born only three years after the death of Copernicus, also deserves special mention. He was not only one of Copernicus's immediate successors, but also one whose painstaking observations and calculations proved the fundamental truth of the Copernican system. If Copernicus is the father of modern astronomy from the viewpoint of its fundamental heliocentric conception, Tycho Brahe may justly be called the father of modern practical astronomy.

If "the proper study of mankind is man," William Harvey (1578-1657), the English physician who discovered the circulation of blood, approached the study of man in a scientific manner and laid the foundation for the modern sciences of physiology and biology.

Different branches of modern science had different birthdays, but directly or indirectly their origins may be traced to the Copernican era. His treatise "Concerning the Revolutions of the Heavenly Spheres" gave birth to revolutions in other branches of science besides astronomy. Thus, as the civilized world of today pays tribute to Copernicus, it may appropriately regard this anniversary as the quadricentennial of modern science.

DIALOGVS
DE SYSTEMATE MVNDI,
Autore
GALILÆO GALILÆI LYNCEO,
SERENISSIMO
FERDINANDO II. HETRVR MAGNO-DVCI
dicatus.

ARISTOT. CL. PTOLEM. N. COPERNICVS.

Augustæ Treboc.
Impensis BONAVENTVRÆ et ABRAHAMI ELZEVIR
Bibliopolar. Leydens.

Anno S. 1635

[26]

The title page of Galileo's famous Dialog about the two Principal Systems of the Universe *(Ptolemaic and Copernican), 1635 edition, first published in the Italian in 1632. The engraving shows Aristotle, Ptolemy and Copernicus. Out of over 300 known likenesses of Copernicus, most of them variations of only a few probably authentic portraits, this is one of the very earliest.*

In the left hand Copernicus holds a device, with which he is often portrayed, illustrating one of his astronomical principles of planetary motions. The sun in the center, around it a large circle of planetary motion, and around that, in turn, another planet moving in a smaller circle or epicycle. The late Prof. Ludwik A. Birkenmajer introduced a new word—concentrobiepicyclic—which is descriptive of the principle and which has been generally accepted by scientists.

In the days of Galileo the Copernican theory was still a revolutionary and dangerous doctrine, upheld only by the most daring spirits at the risk of their own safety. Galileo's Dialog, *which favored the Copernican system in a very subtle but masterly manner, created such a tumult of applause throughout Europe that it brought its author before the Inquisition for the second time; this time resulting in imprisonment in his own residence for the rest of his life. However, he was not burned at the stake as some people still erroneously believe.*

*Photostatic reproduction of the title page of Nicholas Coper-
nicus's* De Revolutionibus Orbium Coelestium *first edition
(1543). Notations in long hand, and at bottom in print, tell
the complete story of its peregrination. The writing at the
bottom, later crossed out, says in Latin:* Reverendo D. [domino]
Georgio Donder canonico Varmiensi amico suo Joachimus
Rheticus d:d:. *Meaning: "To Reverend Mr. George Donder,
Canon of Varmia, from [or to] his friend Joachim Rheticus."
The initials* d:d: *stood for a Latin dedicatory formula—*Donat
Dedicat. *This dedicatory inscription was later crossed out and,
in another hand, above, we see the legend:* Collegii Bruns-
bergensis Societatis Jesu. *This copy was apparently donated to
the Jesuit College of Brunsberg (present Baunsberg) in Varmia.
The college was still in existence in 1939 as* Lyceum Hosianum.
*It was founded, after 1551, by the Polish Cardinal, Stanislaw
Hozjusz (1504-1579), who was then Bishop of Varmia. Carried
by Gustavus Adolphus to Sweden in 1626, the book found its
way finally to the Library of the Royal University of Uppsala,
Sweden. One copy of the first edition is also in possession of
the New York Public Library.*

NICOLAI CO
PERNICI TORINENSIS
DE REVOLVTIONIBVS ORBI-
um coelestium, Libri VI.

Habes in hoc opere iam recens nato, & ædito,
studiose lector, Motus stellarum, tam fixarum,
quàm erraticarum, cum ex ueteribus, tum etiam
ex recentibus obseruationibus restitutos: & no-
uis insuper ac admirabilibus hypothesibus or-
natos. Habes etiam Tabulas expeditissimas, ex
quibus eosdem ad quoduis tempus quàm facilli
me calculare poteris. Igitur eme, lege, fruere.

ἀγεωμέτρητος οὐδεὶς εἰσίτω.

Collegij Braunsbergensis Societatis Iesu.

Norimbergæ apud Ioh. Petreium,
Anno M. D. XLIII.

Reverendo D: Georgio
Donner canonico Varmiensi
amico suo Ioachimus
R Gasius Tr:

[29]

SARMATICUS ASTRONOMUS

No. 2391.   16. Oct.

B. Mithobio.

Epist. lib. II. p. 333 sqq. (edit. Lond. lib. II. ep. 337.)

D. Burcardo Mithobio.

S. D. Et optarim te hac iter facere, et venienti
multa de insidiosissimis actionibus narrarem, et
de caeteris rebus, quae literis committi non pos-
sunt. De concionatore cum *Luthero* et D. *Pome-
rano* deliberabo, quos scio cupere optime con-
sultum Ecclesiis vestris, et Illustrissimam Domi-
nam *), piis votis Deo commendare. De monasteriis quod significas, quosdam esse cunctantio-
res, relinquamus illis suam sapientiam, fortassis
volunt σπεύδειν βραδέως, etsi saepe iam magno
cum dolore expertus sum, admodum esse incon-
stantes τῶν ἀρχόντων animos. Vos initio pu-
gnate, ut populi Ecclesiae, seu, ut vocantur, πα-
ροικίαι bene instaurentur et constituantur. Ple-
rique Principes etiam ante hoc tempus multo fue-
runt in diripiendis Monasteriis diligentiores, quam
in constituendis παροικίας et scholis. Sed expe-
ctemus venientem annum, qui fortassis excutiet
nostris Heroibus veternum, ludos, voluptates,
amores, rixas. Hactenus alii saevierunt in Ecclesias, alii finxerunt corruptelas doctrinae, certarunt obscoenis libellis; finxerunt insulsos dialo-
gos, oblectarunt se Venereis voluptatibus, negle-
xerunt Ecclesias et scholas, certarunt ambitione.
Nunc Nemesis attrahit non contemnendum hostem.
Sed oremus Deum, ut tegat Ecclesias et nostros
etiam ad vera τῆς θεοσεβίας officia exuscitet. Vidi
dialogum, et fui dissuasor editionis. Fabula per
sese paulatim consilescet; sed quidam putant esse
egregium κατόρθωμα rem tam absurdam ornare,
sicut ille Sarmaticus Astronomus **), qui movet
terram et figit Solem. Profecto sapientes guber-
natores deberent ingeniorum petulantiam coher-
cere. Bene vale, die 16. Octobris.

Page 679 of vol. IV of Corpus Reformatorum, *containing a letter (of
Oct. 16, 1541) from Philipp Melanchthon to a Mr. Burcard Mithobius,
with first historic reference to "that Sarmatian astronomer who is trying to stop the sun and move the earth." The underscoring is that of
the present writer. The two stars after* Astronomus *were inserted by
later Editor, Bretschneider, giving the name of Copernicus in the footnote—not shown in this photostatic copy.*

[32]

Part II

SARMATICUS ASTRONOMUS

Sarmaticus Astronomus,
qui movet terram et figit Solem.

          —PHILIPP MELANCHTHON

Wstrzymal slonce, wzruszyl ziemie,
Polskie wydalo go plemie.

    "The sun he bade to stop, and at his
    bidding the earth began to spin—
    Poland has nurtured him."

EVER since the scientific world rediscovered Copernicus and the Polish nation built a public monument in Warsaw to honor the great astronomer, the Germans at first began to question his Polish nationality and then even advanced arguments that he might have been German. Their arguments have been: that he spelled his name with a double "p" (Coppernicus or Koppernigk); that Silesia, the land whence his ancestors came, is German; that Torun (Thorn), the place of his birth, and Krakow (Cracow), the Polish center of learning where he received his first university education, are German cities; that everything worth-while in Poland is German.

Prior to the XIX century, there was no question of Copernicus's nationality. The first testimony we have about his Sar-

matian ancestry comes from no other than the great German
theologian and reformer, Philipp Melanchthon (1497-1560),
who derisively referred to his contemporary scientist as "that
Sarmatian astronomer, who is trying to stop the sun and move
the earth"—calling the whole conception such an absurd
notion *(rem tam absurdum)*.[9] It is not our purpose here to
enter into polemics with a view of proving or disproving German claims, either of territorial or cultural implications. But
rather, within the limited space at our disposal, to collate such
information as would enable the reader to have a better understanding of the family and territorial backgrounds of our
subject.

THE CRADLE OF THE FAMILY: SILESIA AND KRAKOW

There are some things about the life, relationships and associations of Copernicus that we are quite sure of and have docu-
mentary evidence for; there are other things that we do not
know all about, and volumes of words set forth in many languages have not given us as yet a complete answer; and there
are still other things that are buried in the pre-historic past
and perhaps will never be known.

Copernicus is a simplified Latin version which he himself
assumed and finally used. It is not the name, in its final form,
that he took from his father and used all his life. In his younger
years he would sign himself most frequently as Coppernic or
Coppernicus; in his later years, with a single "p"—in the
Polish version Copernic, and in Latin version Copernicus. His
brother Andreas spelled it still differently. Names in those
days were not typewritten or spelled out. They were entered
by scribes approximately as they sounded; and when copied,
changes occurred. What the name intrinsically means, where

it comes from, its changes and evolution, we shall briefly discuss later.

But we are certain that his ancestors came from (originally Polish) Silesia and that his great-grandfather became a citizen of Krakow in 1396. We know that from an official document of Krakow for the year 1396 which states that, "Nicolaus Koppirnig received the right of citizenship. Dambraw[10] vouched for his birth certificate." In the absence of actual birth certificate the testimony of a respectable local citizen was sufficient. The founding of Krakow, incidentally—like that of Rome—is enveloped in myth and tradition. When contem-

A specimen of Copernicus's handwriting and signature in the year 1539.

[35]

porary sources mention Poland in the tenth century, Krakow was already a stronghold. Boleslaw Chrobry (966-1025), the first crowned king of Poland, made it the seat of a bishopric in the year 1000. Silesia on the other hand, especially that part of Silesia from which Copernicus's ancestors came to settle in Krakow, was a land contested by the Slav and the Teuton for many centuries. Originally it was inhabited by two Slavonic tribes *(Slezanie* and *Opolanie)* out of which, together with other tribes to the east and northeast, arose the historic Poland in the tenth century. From the tenth to the fourteenth century Silesia was ruled by princes of the original Polish Piast dynasty, then passed under Bohemian suzerainty, and later under Germany. Blood and names of the former inhabitants thereof are hidden in nebulous past of the pre-nationalistic and even pre-historic era.

The Name Kopernik and Its Meaning

Not far northwest from Katowice there is still (or was in recent times) a parish village by the name of Koppernig, whence the ancestors of Copernicus came. The name of the village, not unlike that of the astronomer's family, has been variously spelled. A large German atlas of Silesia, published by Wieland in Nuremberg in 1731, spells it Kopernik.

While at present towns and villages often are named after their founders, formerly it was the residents—when they moved to other places—who were frequently named after towns and villages of their former domicile. Thus George Joachim (Rheticus), the contemporary admirer of Copernicus, was named after his native province of Rhaetia. That the family name of Kopernik comes from the village by that name, or closely resembling it in spelling or sound, of that we are fairly certain. But there are differences of opinion as to the origin of the name of the village itself. There are at least two

[36]

plausible explanations. One interpretation is that it comes from the occupation of coppersmithing—from Latin *cuprum,* through German *Kupfer*. Kopernik in old Polish also meant a dealer or worker in metal, more particularly in copper. When the Polish Piast princes invited German colonists (or the latter came uninvited) to settle in Silesia, they must have introduced coppersmithing, from which industrial occupation the village probably took its name. In fact Nicholas Copernicus comes of a family of merchants with a long tradition in metal trading. The earliest (1448) extant information about his father shows that he was a merchant in Krakow and a dealer in copper—buying it in Hungary and selling in Danzig and Torun. Another plausible explanation is that the name of the village comes from a plant that was profusely growing there. Kopernik, Koperek, Kopr and Koprnik in Polish—also similarly in other Slavonic languages—means simply dill such as is used in dill pickling. Be it as it may, although the present writer is inclined more towards the occupational interpretation, it is interesting to note that the family name of the great astronomer's ancestors was variously spelled but always in close resemblance to the sound of the Polish or Slavonic dill, viz.: Coprnik, Copirnik, Copernik, Copernick, Koprnik, Kopirnik, Koppirnik, Koppernik, Koppernigk, Kopernik— plus a few other variants.[11] Names seem to have curious fashions of their own; Shakespeare's name has been spelled differently, Smith and Brown have had their variants; and even Field in England was once Feild.

"ON THE MOTHER'S SIDE"

On the mother's side our astronomer's ancestral antecedents cannot be traced with the degree of certainty with which we followed his male lineage from Silesia to Krakow, then to Torun. However, contemporarily the family was well known.

Nicholas Copernicus or rather Kopernik, the Elder, married (between 1461 and 1464) a Barbara Watzelrod, the daughter of a patrician merchant of Torun, Lucas and Katherine Watzelrod. This name has also had many variants: Watzelrode, Weisselrode, Watzelrod, Wazelrod, Waczelrod, Waczenrod, Wacelrod, etc. There is no certainty as to where this family came from. Some advance the theory that it came originally also from Silesia; others, that it came from East Prussia; still others, that it is an old Masovian Polish family. A local German historian, Gottfried Centner (1712-1774), who also devoted considerable attention to genealogies of prominent Torun families in the past, says that the astronomer's mother's mother (grandmother Katherine) came of the family of Modlibog.[12] If that be so, Modlibog (in Polish, literally, *Praygod*) is a family well known in the history of Poland since 1271.

Family names on both the father's and mother's side disappeared with the death of Nicholas Copernicus and his uncle, Bishop Lucas Watzelrod. Nicholas Copernicus or Kopernik, the Elder, and Barbara Watzelrod had four children, two sons and two daughters. Both sons, Andreas and Nicholas, were churchmen and therefore unmarried and left no descendants. Lucas Watzelrod and Katherine Modlibog, the astronomer's maternal grandparents had only one son Lucas,[13] our friend Bishop of Varmia. That the Watzelrod family was distinguished, is reflected in the provincial records. Of Lucas Watzelrod, the Elder, they have this to say: that he was "devout and honest" (this much apparently could not be said of other merchants), that he was "a faithful servant of the Polish king," that he fought valiantly and must have been well-to-do as he advanced his own money for the defense of the city; and of his spouse, Katherine *née* Modlibog, that "she was the crown of all Torun beauties."

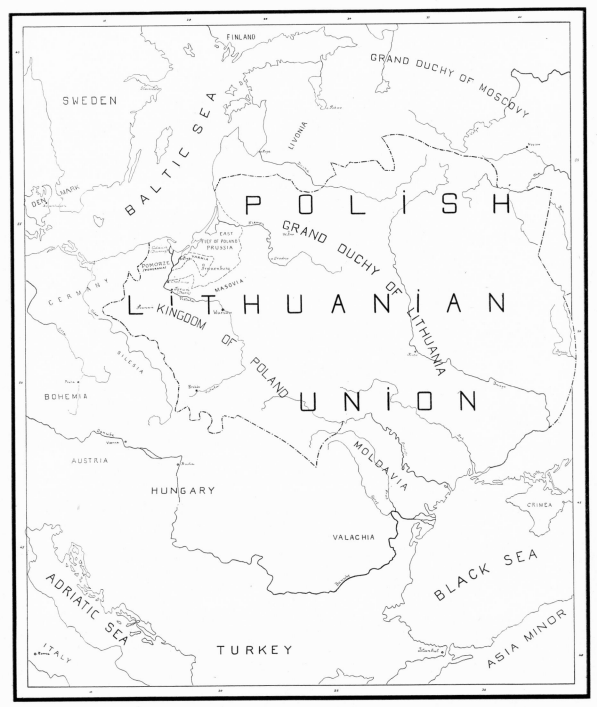

FINLAND

SWEDEN

GRAND DUCHY OF MOSCOVY

BALTIC SEA

LIVONIA

DEN   MARK

P O L I S H

EAST
FIEF OF POLAND
PRUSSIA

GRAND DUCHY OF

POMORZE
(POMERANIA)

VARMIA

GERMANY

Chelmno
Torun
(Thorn)

MASOVIA

L I T H U A N I A N

KINGDOM

Warsaw

LITHUANIA

SILESIA

OF

BOHEMIA

Krakow

POLAND

U N I O N

DANUBE
Vienna

AUSTRIA

MOLDAVIA

CRIMEA

HUNGARY

VALACHIA

BLACK   SEA

ADRIATIC   SEA

ASIA MINOR

ITALY
Rome

TURKEY

Istanbul

POLAND IN THE DAYS OF COPERNICUS

"Prussian Poland," Torun and Varmia

A. M. Clerke, in Encyclopaedia Britannica on Copernicus, says: "Polish astronomer . . . born . . . at Thorn [Torun] in Prussian Poland." Also gives one of the variants of the name: Koppernigk. All the facts here are correct. It may be added, however, that this "Prussian Poland" or Polish Prussia is Pomorze in Polish, the so-called *Polish Corridor*. But some writers, knowingly or unknowingly, have dropped the word "Poland" and turned the adjective "Prussian" into a noun Prussia. The conclusion seemed to follow then that if Copernicus was born in Prussia, he was Prussian and being Prussian, he must have been German.

A few words about the territorial complex with which Copernicus was associated as a child and then as mature man —i.e. about "Prussian Poland" and Varmia—are essential for better orientation. Let us therefore take a little side trip into that historic "Corridor." Time was when there was no such thing as Prussia, or West Prussia, in the modern sense. For a long time Polish princes and kings ruled in Pomorze, including Masovia where Torun now stands. To the southwest of Pomorze, formerly pastureland and hunting ground of Slavonic tribes, was the Mark of Brandenburg; to the northeast, later known as East Prussia, there lived a pagan Baltic tribe (akin to the Lithuanians) called the Prussians. The Polish Duke Conrad of Masovia had considerable difficulty with these pagans, who frequently would pillage his borderland and kill off the inhabitants. To help him protect his Polish territory against the inroads of these savage Prussians from the northeast, Conrad invited (in 1225/6) the Knights of the Teutonic Order to settle in the district of Chelmno (Kulm) on a "lend-lease" plan. This cure proved much worse than the disease as it turned into the story of the Arab and the camel. These Teutonic Knights exterminated most of the original Prussians, settled the territory (East Prussia) with German colonists, and then turned on their hosts the Poles. They conquered the Polish Pomorze province, including Danzig, and also severed from Poland the Chelmno district, with its center of Tarnowo (meaning in Polish the little town or village of Tarnow), whose name they changed in 1231-33 to Thorn (through Tarn, Torn to Thorn)[14] and which they held until the rebellion against the Order in 1454-66. After the Treaty of Torun of 1466, this city with the entire Pomorze, then called Royal Prussia (later West Prussia), and a part of East Prussia, the duchy-bishopric of Varmia or Ermland (of which Copernicus was a canon), came under Poland where they remained until the first and the second partitions, when they were incorporated in the new Kingdom of Prussia: Varmia and most of Pomorze in 1772, Torun and Danzig in 1793. Torun was afterwards temporarily (1806-15) attached to the Grand Duchy of Warsaw, but in 1815 was granted to Prussia, in which it remained till 1918. The State of Prussia, which played such a large part in the history of modern Germany, arose from the combination of the Mark of Brandenburg and the State of the Teutonic Order in East Prussia, from which the general name was derived. Somehow the name Prussia lingered through historical writings, and "Polish Prussia" or "Prussian Poland" has often been used by foreign writers and historians as synonyms for the Polish Pomorze.

"WRITING ON THE WALL" AND OTHER MEMENTOS

The Cathedral of Frauenburg in the duchy-bishopric of Varmia, had fortifications and towers. One of the towers Copernicus used for his laboratory and astronomical observatory, now known as the Tower of Copernicus *(Turricula Copernici)* which has been turned into a small museum.

[41]

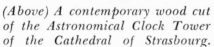

(Above) A contemporary wood cut of the Astronomical Clock Tower of the Cathedral of Strasbourg.

(Right) Copy of selfportrait of Nicholas Copernicus, done by Tobias Stimmer, in 1571, on the Astronomical Clock Tower of the Cathedral of Strasbourg. Lily of the valley may be a symbol of Copernicus's interest in natural philosophy, more particularly in medicine.

Among the mementos there are: a few works from the astronomer's personal library, one set of astronomical tables by Johann de Regio Monte or Regiomontanus (1436-1476) with notes and drawings made by Copernicus, and a piece of an old bent and rusty pipe which he allegedly used as a telescope.

In the Bishop's Chateau at Olsztyn (Allenstein) where Copernicus stayed in 1517-19, 1521 and 1525 during his travels as Canon of Varmia, there is a room which he occupied. On the walls of that room, telltale evidence of his occupancy is offered by scribblings and astronomical notations in his own handwriting. Whenever ideas came to him, he would put them down on margins of books, calendars, and even on walls. This might have been a habit which he acquired during his student days, especially if he lived in a dormitory. . . . Be it as it may, such notations enabled the outstanding Copernican scholar, the late Professor Ludwik A. Birkenmajer who devoted his lifetime for this purpose, to recreate the genesis and progress of the Copernican system—from the last year of Copernicus's student days at the University of Krakow up to the composition of the *De Revolutionibus*.

We stated in the beginning that Copernicus was also an artist. He was; but how good, we do not know. The only evidence we have of his artistic efforts is indirect: a copy of his selfportrait. The original painting or drawing was sent from Danzig by Dr. Tidemann Gise to Tobias Stimmer, who reproduced it (about 1571-74) on the famous astronomical clock tower of the Cathedral of Strasbourg (Strassburg).

There are schools, streets, monuments, tablets and plaques commemorating Copernicus in all sections of Poland. The University of Bologna, already in our time, ordered a Copernicus bust from a Polish sculptor. Hamtramck, Mich., which has a large population of Polish ancestry, gave its sumptuous

"In the year 1500 he went to Rome, where he also lectured on mathematics and astronomy." Although the painter, Wojciech Gerson (1831-1901), has a number of prominent contemporaries present at the lecture (including such celebrities as Leonardo da Vinci, Pope Alexander VI and the astronomer Domenico Maria Novara from Bologna University), it cannot be proved that all of them were present at one time.

*The Copernicus monument which
the Germans erected in Torun,
"as a demonstrable and demonstrative reminder to the Poles that
Torun and its inhabitants, great
and small, have always been and
will also be German."*

*View of the Copernicus classroom in the Cathedral of Learning,
University of Pittsburgh. On the wall, to the left, is a copy of the
famous painting of Copernicus by Jan Matejko. To the right is a
replica of the Jagiellonian golden globe, presented by the
Polish National Alliance of America.*

[45]

Junior High School the name of Copernicus. The University of Pittsburgh has a Copernicus classroom in the Cathedral of Learning. Formerly the desire to commemorate the great astronomer was as slow as the acceptance of his theory.

We shall outline briefly the most characteristic memorials that were written or erected in honor of the famous astronomer through the past four centuries; the earliest, for the most part, consisting of writing on the wall.

He was buried in the Cathedral of Frauenburg near the main altar, and over his grave was placed a simple flagstone on which some kind hand had chiselled out the following simple inscription: "Nicolaus Copernicus died in the year MDXLIII." About fifty years later Marcin Kromer, a Krakovian, Polish historian and statesman and a bishop of Varmia, had a suitable memorial tablet built into the wall of the cathedral; but this tablet was removed by some unknown hand around 1732-34. Further attempts at more imposing commemoration in monuments or plaques on the part of Varmian canons and bishops, including that of Bishop Ignacy Krasicki (1735-1801), resulted only in monumental good will. Also towards the end of the XVI century, a physician and well-to-do citizen of Torun, Melchior Pyrnezjusz, originally from Krakow, erected a Copernicus statue in the St. John's Church in Torun and over the statue put the following characteristic inscription in Latin: "To Nicholas Copernicus of Torun, so renowned in other lands, this monument is erected so that he may not be forgotten in his own motherland." In 1733 a councilman of Torun, Jakob Kazimierz Rubinowski, had this statue "restored and renovated" at his own expense and added a portrait of one of the Polish kings who died in Torun in 1501 and whose heart was buried in that church. Also in the same church, in 1743, Prince Jozef Jablonowski erected another Copernicus statue with the inscription over it in Latin: "To

Nicholas Copernicus, Polish Philosopher and Eternal Ornament of Torun."

Among the private busts of Copernicus in Krakow and in other Polish cities, the one erected in 1823 by the Reverend Father Count Sebastjan Sierakowski, Rector of the University of Krakow, deserves especial consideration. It stands near the high altar in the university church of St. Ann in Krakow. Over it, on the wall, there are two inscriptions. One in Latin: "Nicholas Copernicus, the ornament, the honor and the glory of his country, his city and his university." The other in Polish:

> *Polskie wydalo go plemie,*
> *Wstrzymal slonce, wzruszyl ziemie.*

which, in free translation, means:

> "The sun he bade to stop, and at his bidding
> the earth began to spin—
> Poland has nurtured him."

Because of its brevity and simplicity, this epigram, in the inverted order, became an adage and a property of the entire Polish nation. In the inverted order it reads:

> *Wstrzymal slonce, wzruszyl ziemie,*
> *Polskie wydalo go plemie.*

Up to this time Polish writers on Copernicus have been wondering as to who the author of this apt epigram was. They searched high and low, in fiction and poetry, and finally declared that the author is unknown. They have known, of course, of the uncomplimentary sentiments expressed by Philipp Melanchthon in his full sentence; but this Polish epigram is so *Polish* that it did not occur to them that anybody but a Pole could be its original author. Great truths, simply

[47]

expressed, whether intentionally or unintentionally, have a way of crossing national boundaries and of working their way even into sanctuaries.

It is one of the ironies of *Copernicana* that the original author of this Polish epigram was a German, Philipp Melanchthon; a German and a Protestant, the kernel of whose sentiments unwittingly expressed was translated from Latin into the Polish, by a prince of Polish learning and a Polish Roman Catholic churchman (Reverend Father Rector, Count Sebastjan Sierakowski), and inscribed near the high altar in the university church at Krakow. *Sarmaticus Astronomus* (literally, Sarmatian astronomer), was freely and poetically translated into *Polskie wydalo go plemie* (literally, the Polish race has nurtured him); and the rest of Melanchthon's sentence, *qui movet terram et figit Solem* (literally, who is trying to move the earth and stop the sun), was put in the past tense and given a literal translation. Great scientific truth, poetically expressed; that is exactly what Copernicus did in his heliocentric system, he stopped the sun and set the earth in motion.

MEDALS

There were also numerous medals struck in commemoration of Copernicus—many in Poland, some in other countries. Among the first medals of the early XVIII century, there was one struck by Christian Wermuth of Gotha (Germany), a court medalist. Judging by the inscription on the reverse side, it is not certain whether the court medalist wanted to honor or to ridicule the astronomer. The inscription reads, in German: "According to opinion of the learned, it is the sun and not the earth that turns round. Everybody has his worm, Copernicus has his."

In 1818 a Parisian medalist, Durand, decided to honor, each through a separate medal, one hundred great men of all

[48]

nations. Among the first twenty-five were two Poles: Tadeusz Kosciuszko and Nicholas Copernicus. The first Durand medal of Copernicus met with a mishap. It bore the inscription: *Natus Torunii in Prussia*. When somebody called Durand's attention to the fact that this reference to the name of the place of birth might lead to misleading conclusion as to the nationality of the astronomer, Durand brought out a new edition with the inscription: *Natus Torunii in Polonia*. Other French medalists afterwards followed this "corrected edition" of Durand's.

Public Monuments

All the above tributes were private or strictly local and institutional. The first public monument erected in Poland to honor Copernicus, which was at the same time the very first public monument erected in the capital of Poland by popular subscription, was the one unveiled in Warsaw in 1830.

Just as Copernicus belongs to all mankind, even so this first public monument to him is a product of at least three nationalities: Italo-French, Danish and Polish. Curiously it was Napoleon who gave the idea, the Poles gave the money and put their hearts into it, and the well known Danish sculptor—Bertel Thorwaldsen (1770-1844) the son of an Icelander —shaped the idea and the Polish desires into permanent form.

When Napoleon was in Torun in 1807, he expressed surprise that the fellow countrymen of Copernicus had not so far seen fit to honor this great astronomer by a suitable monument in the town of his birth. Acting upon Napoleon's suggestion, in 1809 a group of Warsaw citizens, headed by Stanislaw Staszic, started to raise funds by public subscription for such a monument in Torun, which was then included in the Grand Duchy of Warsaw. For a while in 1809, due to Napoleonic war operations, the State Council transferred its sessions from War-

The house in which Nicholas Copernicus was born—visited by Napoleon. "When Napoleon was in Torun in 1807, he expressed surprise that the fellow countrymen of Copernicus had not so far seen fit to honor this great astronomer by a suitable monument in the town of his birth."

saw to Torun. Thus Torun became a temporary or quasi capital of the Grand Duchy. The State Council voted an initial sum of money, the cornerstone was laid with impressive ceremonies, and for the balance of funds needed to erect the monument an appeal was made to the public. Although 4,795 Polish zlotys were raised, the turmoil of the period interfered with the completion of the project. When, after the Congress of Vienna (1815), Torun was annexed again to German Prussia, the project was not renewed till 1828. Again Stanislaw Staszic, one of the thirty *Great Men and Women of Poland*, revived the movement by a personal donation of 4,000 Polish zlotys and the monument was unveiled in Warsaw on May 11, 1830, in front of the monumental building devoted to science and learning and which, due to other reasons, bears the name of Staszic—*Palac Staszica.*

The monument bears two inscriptions: one in Latin, *Nicolao Copernico Grata Patria* (to Nicholas Copernicus, Grateful Motherland); the other in Polish: *Mikolajowi Kopernikowi, Rodacy* (to Nicholas Copernicus, His Fellow Countrymen). Later on, in 1900, another monument was erected by the University of Krakow in the courtyard of the university library, sculptured by Cyprian Godebski (1835-1909), who also sculptured the Mickiewicz monument in Warsaw. What has happened to the Copernicus monument in the courtyard of the University of Krakow library, we do not know, for entrance into that courtyard is *verboten* to the Poles. But we do know from Polish refugees who escaped from Warsaw in 1940 that one of the things the Germans did when they occupied Warsaw in September, 1939, was to blot out both inscriptions on the Copernicus monument and to substitute for them one of their own: "To Nicholas Copernicus, the German Nation."[15]

This manifestation of the Poles in 1828-30 was a signal for the methodical Germans to start building one of their own in

The Copernicus monument in the courtyard of the University of Krakow library—the identical university building in which Copernicus studied.

[52]

The Copernicus monument in Warsaw, in front of **Palac Staszica.**

Torun, or rather to finish what the Poles had begun in 1809, as a demonstrable and demonstrative reminder to the Poles that Torun and its inhabitants, great and small, have always been and will always be German. Out of the estimated cost of 10,449 thaler, the King of Prussia gave 3,466 or approximately one-third; the German residents of Torun raised 482 thaler; and the practical City Council, which was planning to build a public well in the city square, anyway, added 654 thaler on the condition, which was carried out, that a well be also incorporated in the monument.

WHY ARE THE POLES PROUD OF COPERNICUS?

They are proud of him, because the whole civilized world claims him as its own; because the man, his interests and his contributions have universal and abiding qualities. Even the common folk, who may not understand his heliocentric system, instinctively feel that through Copernicus they are bound with other nations by spiritual links that have permanent value.

Although Copernicus lived in an age when there was no clear-cut conception of nationality in the modern sense and loyalties and patriotism — in contradistinction to universal intellectual interests—were chiefly local, they are proud of him also for national patriotic reasons: because he was born and raised on the soil they love and have been shedding their blood to keep free; because he received his first instruction and inspiration in an institution, the University of Krakow, which their beloved Queen Jadwiga endowed with her jewels; because his first great teacher, Albert Brudzewski, has become a part of the great tradition of that ancient seat of learning and cultural center of Poland. Also because he, together with his guardian uncle Bishop Lucas, fought that enemy which

[54]

they had been fighting for centuries before and have been fighting all these centuries since: the Knights of the Teutonic Order in all its varied forms. They have a feeling of common heritage and spiritual unity with Copernicus.

A Voice from England Across the Century

After the unsuccessful Insurrection of 1831 a refugee Polish scholar, Col. Lach Szyrma, Professor of the University of Warsaw, found his way to England. In time he mastered the English language and in 1843, on the occasion of the Copernican Tercentenary, delivered in London an impressive lecture on *Copernicus and His Native Land* to the Literary Association of the Friends of Poland.

In the audience there was a Dr. Worthington. So impressed and moved was he by Professor Szyrma's lecture that he improvised a poem as a tribute to the lecturer, to Copernicus and to Poland, and which he delivered immediately after the lecture. The poem was later printed in the *Foreign and Colonial Quarterly Review* (1844, p. 35), also in a pamphlet form.

The present Polish situation is similar to that of 1843. The "earthly empire" of the Polish people "ceased" temporarily; there are even more Polish refugee scholars—from the University of Warsaw and from other universities—both in England and in America; but the Anglo-American association with Poland now has more significant implications than the former *literary association* would seem to indicate. It is therefore eminently fitting and proper that we finish *our* story of *Copernicus and his native land* with Dr. Worthington's *Impromptu*—through courtesy of the Library of Congress:

[55]

If earthly empire with thy people cease,
In one thing, Szyrma, thou mayest yet find peace;
The glorious thought, that in their glowing souls
Lives empire ever 'mid thy deep-wronged Poles;
And if to them the earth be now denied,
Think on it, Szyrma, think with honest pride,
That while the planets circle round the sun,
The race of Polish glory is unrun.
Enthroned with Newton in the starry spheres,
Copernicus unfolds to listening ears
The wondrous laws which Nature bared to him:
And but for him to Newton e'en were dim.
Thus Polish glory blends with God's own might,
And lives in regions of eternal light.

FOOTNOTE REFERENCES

[1] Simon Newcomb (1835-1909), *The Problems of Astronomy*, Report of the Smithsonian Institution for 1896, p. 83.

[2] Nicolaus is the given name most frequently used in the Latinized form. Often a French version, Nicolas, is used as it may also represent a simplified Latin form. For the sake of simplicity and convenience, we shall use the English form, Nicholas, for the given name; and for the surname, the Latinized form of Copernicus, by which he is best known.

[3] The University of Krakow was established in 1364 by the last king of the Polish Piast dynasty, Casimir the Great; it was reorganized and renovated in the year 1400 by King Jagiello, in deference to the wish of Queen Jadwiga (d.1399) who sold her jewels and directed that part of the proceeds be used for the benefit of that university. The balance of the proceeds was distributed to the poor. It is the second oldest university in central Europe and one of the oldest on the continent. Preceding it were: Bologna (end of XII century), Padua (1222), Paris (between 1150 and 1170), Prague (1347), Oxford (end of XII century) and Cambridge (beginning of XIII century). All German universities were organized later: Heidelberg, the oldest, in 1385; Cologne, in 1388; Leipzig, in 1409.

[4] That the University of Krakow, especially its Faculty of Astronomy and Mathematics, was well thought of in other lands, is attested—among others—by a contemporary German writer, Hartman Schedelius. In his *Chronicle of the World* he writes: "Near the Church of St. Ann there is a university, famous for its many great and learned men, where all kinds of arts and sciences are cultivated. Foremost among them is astronomy. In this respect, as I am informed by many people, there is not a single school that is more famous in all the lands of the Germans."
Liber Chronic., Norimb. 1493, fol. 266.

[5] Marcin Bylica, the most outstanding Polish astronomer before Albert Brudzewski, was a former student at the University of Krakow and later a member of its teaching staff. He also lectured on astronomy at the University of Bologna; later became professor of astronomy at the newly-founded university (of temporary existence) at Pressburg (Bratislava), then under Hungary, and at Buda. Bylica was one of the first alumni benefactors of his *Alma Mater Cracoviensis*.

[6] The office of canon, although a part of the Church hierarchy, did not require that its incumbent be a fully ordained priest. Despite the earlier assertions of some Polish writers on Copernicus, later occasionally echoed by other writers, Copernicus was not a priest in the full sense of the word; a churchman, but not a priest.

[7] In 1908 there was discovered in the State Archives of Sweden at Stockholm, a most interesting document that throws additional light on Copernicus's active part in contemporary political events. It was a complaint against the predatory inroads of the Teutonic Order and a petition addressed to Sigismund I, King of Poland, asking for help. Dated July 22, 1516, the petition was drawn in Copernicus's own handwriting, in Latin, in behalf of the Chancery of the Bishopric of Varmia. Apparently clean copy was made and dispatched to the king and this original draft remained in Copernicus's own library, which was carried to Sweden by Gustavus Adolphus in 1626.
After a documented complaint, mentioning names and places, Copernicus calls these Knights of the Teutonic Order *latrones* (robbers), and on behalf of his colleagues concludes as follows:

[57]

"We are offering our loyal services and even our very lives, to your Majesty whom we regard as our most gracious Lord" *(offerentes fidelia servitia nostra et ipsam vitam nostram eidem Maiestati Vestre, quam ut Dominum nostrum clementissimum colimus.)*

[8] *Der Narr will die ganze Kunst Astronomiæ umkehren.* Martin Luther's *Tischreden*, vol. IV, p. 575.

[9] Philipi Melanchtonis *Opera*, ed. Carolus Gottlieb Bretschneider, 1837, *Corpus Reformatorum* vol. IV p. 679. (See photographic reproduction of the page referred to).
Another German, sometimes even called "the Great," Frederick II (1712-1786), King of Prussia, in writing to Voltaire (Dec. 11, 1773) as one cynic to another after the first partition of Poland which he "rescued" from all kinds of tyranny, referred to it as "the country which produced Copernicus"—*un pays qui avait produit un Copernic (Oeuvres Posthumes de Frederic II Roi de Prussie,* Berlin ed. 1788, vol. IX p. 208). Even sixty years later a celebrated German historian of literature, Johann Ludwig Wachler (in his monumental *Geschichte der Literatur*, 1833, vol. IV, p. 263), wrote: "Among other nations [which have great sons to be proud of] Poland has a full right to be proud of her Nicholas Copernicus of Torun" *(mit vollem Recht stoltz auf ihren Nicolaus Copernicus aus Thorn).* Even several decades later, Friedrich Wilhelm Nietzsche (1844-1900), the noted German philosopher, paid a tribute to Copernicus as a Pole by saying: ". . . he (Boscovich) and the Pole Copernicus have hitherto been the greatest and most successful opponents of ocular evidence." [Roger Joseph Boscovich (1711?-1787) was an eminent Serbo-Croat scientist.] The *Authorized English Translations of Nietzsche's Works,* by Oscar Levy, New York, 1909-13, 18 vols. vol. XII *Beyond Good and Evil,* p. 19.

[10] Dambraw, the root word for Dabrowski, in later Polish orthography was spelled Dabrowa.

[11] The ponderous German scholarship, in trying to evolve German nationality out of the name of Copernicus, leaned heavily on Slavonic philology through the reasoning that his ancestors' name was spelled with a double "p." As the name with a double "p" could not be Polish, they argued, it must have therefore been German.
Now, there are two difficulties with the conclusion of this reasoning. First, that the family name of Kopernik—Koppirnig or even Koppernigk—was derived from the name of the village and not the other way round. Even if the name of the village is of German origin, it does not follow that all its former inhabitants, surnamed after the place of their former domicile, were necessarily German. Secondly, that we have numerous instances of indisputably Polish historic names misspelled beyond recognition. Thus Bernard Wapowski (as Polish as Paderewski), a life-long friend of Copernicus, had his name spelled even by his Polish contemporaries in such ways as Vapouskij, Vapovskij, Vapovssi, Vapovsky, and Vapovssky. Through philological reasoning one could make out any nationality from one of these variants, any nationality but Polish.

[12] Katherine Modlibog was previously married to a Pek or Penk.

[13] Besides Barbara, the mother of our astronomer, the Watzelrod's had one or possibly two other daughters. One of them married a Maciej Konopacki, Chamberlain of Chelmno. One of the Konopacki's daughters, in turn, married a Sebastjan Czapski. The male descendants of the Czapski's (i.e. collateral descendants of Nicholas Copernicus), have played prominent roles in Polish history as statesmen, soldiers and philanthropists up to the present time. One of them, Count Emeryk Czapski (1828-96), founded a museum bearing his name and bequeathed it, together with a

rich numismatic collection, to the city of Krakow. The widow of his elder son, Count Karol Jan Aleksander Czapski (1860-1904), is now a refugee in New York and at this writing happens to be a neighbor of the present writer.

[14] The later re-Polonization process from Thorn was: Thorunia, Thorun, Torun. There is difference of opinion among historians as to the exact name of the original Polish settlement on which Torun was built. At least one writer on Copernicus credits the first Polish historian, Jan Dlugosz (1415-1480), with having mentioned "Torun on the Vistula" in connection with historical events of 1192. Upon checking up on the original Latin text of Dlugosz, the present writer discovered that Dlugosz had his geography mixed up, placed another town on the Vistula where it did not belong, did not mention Torun at all, and only a later editor of Dlugosz's works put Torun in the footnote—thinking that the historian had this town on the Vistula in mind.

[15] A very careful search failed to reveal a single monument in honor of Copernicus either in Berlin or in any other German city.

Bibliographical Suggestions and Comments

The literature on the subject of Nicholas Copernicus is very extensive—running, literally, into thousands of volumes, special articles, monographs, chapters in histories of astronomy, in biographies of scientists etc.; but its value is strikingly unequal and there is not a single definitive, up-to-date, objective biography in any language—not even in Polish.

The most comprehensive single work up to 1884 and still useful on the bibliographical information, that of Dr. Leopold Prowe, has this shortcoming that it is warped by polemics in favor of his pet theory that Copernicus was a Teuton. Also has many errors in the scientific phases.

The greatest Copernican scholar so far has been the late Ludwik A. Birkenmajer (d. 1929), professor at the University of Krakow, who had written several volumes—a few of which are of monumental import and proportions—and dozens of monographic contributions. Unfortunately: (1) he wrote most of his best works in Polish and therefore they are inaccessible to foreign scholars; (2) his definitive biography of Copernicus, giving a synthesis of all his lifetime researches, has not been published and reposes (or reposed till 1939) in the manuscript form at the University of Krakow library; (3) his only attempt at synthesis was a popular book of 126 pages written on demand in 1923 (*Mikolaj Kopernik, Jako Uczony, Tworca i Obywatel*. Krakow, The Polish Academy, 1923) and is quite inadequate as a single work.

Most of our current biographical sketches available to the average American reader show confusion and give, with solid information, plenty of misinformation. One important American encyclopaedia, for example, puts Torun in Poland, but makes Copernicus study medicine in Krakow (which is not true) and places the well-known Thorwaldsen monument of

Copernicus in Krakow instead of Warsaw. Another important encyclopaedia refers to Copernicus as "a celebrated Polish astronomer, born at Thorn, a Prussian [?] town on the Vistula, at that time belonging to Poland." And then informs the reader that Copernicus "was instructed in the Latin and Greek languages at home." Perhaps its does not matter much, but the fact is that Copernicus began to study his Greek only a an university student in Italy—possibly already at Bologna, and definitely at Padua in 1501-03. The only recent book in the English language devoted exclusively to Copernicus and which makes an attempt at synthesis (Angus Armitage, *Copernicus—The Founder of Modern Astronomy*) relied so "principally" (as the author admits) on Dr. Prowe in biographical data as to state even that Krakow "was founded by Germans" (p. 44). It may be strange but among the short encyclopaedic articles, one of the very best is in *Enciclopedia Italiana* on *Nicolo Copernico* by Guido H. D'Arturo, Professor of Astronomy at the University of Bologna. A well-balanced bibliography accompanies the article.

The following selected list of reading references, with such comments as may seem justified, will be helpful to a reader who may want more information of a general nature on the subject of Copernicus and his life and work, and on the Ptolemaic and Copernican systems of astronomy.

In English

1. *Encyclopaedia Britannica.* Copernicus, Astronomy (History of Astronomy), and Index references to Copernicus, his predecessors and successors.

2. *Great Men and Women of Poland.* Edited by Stephen P. Mizwa, The Macmillan Company, New York, 1941, pp. 397. Chapter on Nicholas Copernicus with illustration, pp. 37-50, by a Polish scholar who for the time being remains anonymous.

3. Ernest R. Trattner, *The Story of the World's Great Thinkers,* The New Home Library, New York, 1938, pp. 426. The first chapter, pp. 11-45, is on Nicholas Copernicus.

> Despite its numerous errors, resulting from attempts at emphasis and oversimplification, this chapter is a very good popular introduction to a better understanding of the Ptolemaic and Copernican systems of the universe.

4. Dorothy Stimson, Ph.D., *The Gradual Acceptance of the Copernican Theory of the Universe,* a doctoral dissertation, New York, 1917, pp. 147. No longer carried by trade selling agents but copies can still be obtained at $1.50 each from: Dean Dorothy Stimson, Goucher College, Baltimore, Md.

> A fine and thoroughly reliable piece of work, well documented, preceded by a brief historical sketch of the heliocentric theory of the universe.

5. John L. E. Dreyer, *History of the Planetary System from Thales to Kepler,* Cambridge University Press, 1906. Out of print now but can be consulted in libraries.

> One of the best in the field of astronomy in general.

6. Angus Armitage, *Copernicus—The Founder of Modern Astronomy,* George Allen and Unwin, London, 1938, pp. 183.

> More useful to students of astronomy than to the general reader. Except for a brief French summary of one of Birkenmajer's works, the author was thoroughly unfamiliar with the research work of Polish Copernican scholars.

7. Edward Rosen (translator), *Three Copernican Treatises* (The Commentariolus of Copernicus, The Letter Against Werner, The Narratio Prima of Rheticus), Columbia University Press, New York, 1939.

> Translation of the original texts.

8. Arthur Berry, *A Short History of Astronomy,* New York, 1910.

9. A. Wolf, *A History of Science, Technology, and Philosophy in the 16th and 17th Centuries,* New York, 1935.

In Polish

1. Ks. Ignacy Polkowski, *Zywot Mikolaja Kopernika* (The Life-Story of Nicholas Copernicus), Gniezno, 1873, pp. 356.

   The first good biography of Copernicus in the Polish language, well documented. Though superseded by works with more discriminating evaluation of sources, it is still very useful. However, very few copies are available in America.

2. Ks. Ignacy Polkowski (compiler), *Kopernikijana czyli materjaly do pism i zycia Mikolaja Kopernika* (Copernicana or materials on the writings and life of Nicholas Copernicus), Gniezno, 1873-75, 3 vols.

   Valuable Copernicana materials in Polish.

3. Ludwik A. Birkenmajer, *Mikolaj Kopernik—Studya nad Pracami Kopernika oraz Materyaly Biograficzne, Czesc I* (Nicholas Copernicus — Studies on the Writings of Copernicus and Biographical Materials, Part I), The Polish Academy of Sciences, Krakow, 1900, pp. 711, *quarto*.

   A monumental piece of work, in which the author gives some of the preliminary results of his research on the genesis and development of the Copernican heliocentric system. Part II, which was to give a definitive biography of Copernicus, was not published. The manuscript was deposited in the University of Krakow library.

4. Ludwik A. Birkenmajer, *Mikolaj Kopernik—Jako Uczony, Tworca i Obywatel* (Nicholas Copernicus—as a Scientist, Scientific Creator and Citizen), The Polish Academy of Sciences, Krakow, 1923, pp. 126.

   A popular monograph of this great Copernican scholar. Not as valuable to scholars as some of the other scientific monographs.

5. Ludwik A. Birkenmajer, *Stromata Copernicana*, Krakow, 1924.
   A continuation of the Polish Academy publication of 1900.

6. *Mikolaj Kopernik, Lwowski Komitet Obchodu 450 Rocznicy Urodzin M. Kopernika* (Nicholas Copernicus, published by the Lwow

Committee Commemorating the 450th Anniversary of the Birth of N. Copernicus), Lwow, 1924, pp. 246.

> Includes ten commemorative essays dealing with various aspects of the great astonomer's work. Of unequal length and value. Among the outstanding are: Prof. Fr. Bujak's essay on *Copernicus's Treatise on Money* and a *Copernicana Bibliography* prepared by W. Bruchnalski. The selected bibliography, covering the period 1543-1923 and limited for the most part to Polish works, is well annotated and consists of 588 items.

7. Jeremi Wasiutynski, *Kopernik: Tworca Nowego Nieba* (Copernicus: The Creator of the New Heavens), pub. J. Przeworski, Warsaw, 1938, pp. 666.

> A remarkable performance of a young man, who attempted to write a definitive biography of Copernicus with the aid of the new sociologico-psychological tools. The subject is perhaps overpsychoanalyzed. In trying to reach different conclusions from previous Copernican scholars, the author is often rasping. Reads like an historical novel, although its scientific value, for the most part, is much greater. Taken in conjunction with other works as correctives, it will have a permanent place in the Polish literature on the subject.

8. Zygmunt Batowski, *Wizerunki Kopernika* (Portraits of Copernicus), Torun, 1933, pp. 99.

> Contains 18 illustrations with descriptive and historical sketches. Very good as far as it goes.

Part III

PROGRAM SUGGESTIONS

As this brochure went to press (December 1, 1942), the Kosciuszko Foundation, which initiated the Copernican Quadricentennial, was already in possession of several hundred letters from heads of American colleges and universities, of junior and state teachers colleges as well as of leading higher institutions of learning in Canada,— all enthusiastically endorsing the project of the Copernican Quadricentennial and expressing a desire to join the Kosciuszko Foundation in arranging in each case some appropriate celebration or tribute to Copernicus on this important anniversary. It was also evident that there will be citizens committees in hundreds of communities scattered throughout the United States that will arrange such celebrations either jointly with local colleges and universities or as separate community projects.

On the occasion of the Copernican Quadricentennial, the Polish Institute of Arts and Sciences in New York, as one of its cooperative contributions, is planning: First, to arrange a series of lectures by outstanding scholars, on Copernicus and Poland in the Copernican Era. Second, to publish a symposium of monographs on Life and Work of Copernicus. Polish scholars of the University of Krakow, in conjunction with the Polish Academy, were planning, on the occasion of the Copernican Quadricentennial in 1943, to bring out an edition of complete works of Copernicus, *Opera Omnia*, incorporating the latest results of scientific research. The war interfered and this symposium of Polish scholars in America

[65]

will be a modest expression of the formerly more ambitious plan.

Because most of the colleges and universities now operate under the accelerated war program, with the current school year ending early in May, a good many heads of these institutions asked us if they could hold their Copernican programs earlier in May or after May 24th. The answer, of course, is Yes. We are celebrating not so much the death of the great astronomer as the publication of his immortal work, *De Revolutionibus Orbium Coelestium,* and the birth of modern science of astronomy, of modern science in general. The 400th anniversary of the death of Copernicus is only a prompting occasion.

Invariably these expressions of desire to join in this national tribute to Copernicus were accompanied by requests for more information about the subject, for program suggestions, sometimes even for recommendations of speakers. Occasionally an observation was made that, due to the crowded calendar, only a chapel period could be devoted to the Copernican program—with one short address on Copernicus and some reference to other Poles and their contributions to civilization.

We are therefore suggesting two alternative programs: a short program suitable for a chapel period, not lasting more than thirty minutes; and a full Copernican Quadricentennial Program for an hour and a half to two hours.

I. Short Program

1. "The Broken Note" Signal.
2. The American and Polish National Anthems.
3. *Gaude Mater Polonia.*
4. Address: Nicholas Copernicus.

In case the speaker should like to mention other Poles and their contributions, the most accessible information may be found in a single volume: "Great Men and Women of Poland" edited by the present writer and published by The Macmillan Company, New York, 1942.

The full program as outlined, if time permits, can be easily arranged by universities, colleges, schools and citizens committees—with such modifications, extensions or simplifications as local conditions warrant or make necessary.

II. The Copernican Quadricentennial Program

1. "The Broken Note" Signal (trumpet).

2. The American and Polish National Anthems.

3. *Gaude Mater Polonia.*

4. Address: Nicholas Copernicus and His Contributions.

5. Short Pageant: The Initiation of Copernicus into the University of Krakow (optional).

6. Address: The Death of Copernicus, and the Birth of Modern Science.

7. Address: The Universality of Science, Its Place in Modern Life and in the World of Tomorrow (optional).

8. The *Alma Mater* song of given college or university, or some patriotic hymn of universal appeal in which the audience may join (e.g. "America" or "Star Spangled Banner").

9. *Copernicana* Exhibit.

EXPLANATIONS

(1) "The Broken Note" Signal.

In the main square of the ancient city of Krakow stands St. Mary's Church, from one of whose towers a trumpeter plays a signal, known as the *hejnal,* every hour on the hour of day and of night.

The tradition of this "Trumpeter of Krakow" — made known to America by Prof. Eric P. Kelly through his book under that title, the Newbury Medal winner for 1928—goes back to days long before Copernicus, to the days of the great Tartar invasion of Poland in the year 1241. The function of the trumpeter was to give a signal when he saw an approaching foe and thus warn the inhabitants of Krakow. One day, as the Tartars were approaching the city square, the trumpeter gave the signal. Before he finished it, a Tartar arrow pierced his throat. Hence, the broken note, the unfinished melody. That's the traditional basis of the "broken note" *hejnal.* Historically, it was introduced as a permanent institution by Louis the Great, King of Hungary, who was also the absentee ruler of Poland (1370-82) the father of Jadwiga Queen of Poland (1384-99). In Polish *hejnal,* it most probably comes from the Hungarian *hajnal,* meaning the morning star—planet Venus—dawn, daybreak, hence figuratively the *reveille.*

When the Germans occupied Krakow in September, 1939, they silenced the trumpeter in Krakow, but his melody lingers on. There are echoes of it in America. At Vassar College, for example, the broken note *hejnal* is played as a call to chapel. This old melody with rich historic associations seems to us to be most appropriate as an opening note for any Copernican program.

(2) The National Anthems may be played by an orchestra or sung by a choir or the audience.

(3) *Gaude Mater Polonia.* Sung in Krakow in the student

days of Copernicus, this is one of the three oldest Polish hymns dating back to the XIII century. It originated as a hymn to St. Stanislaus on the occasion of his canonization in 1253. It was in time adopted by the University of Krakow and was sung on all dignified academic occasions: such as opening and closing of the school year, welcoming distinguished foreign guests, granting of honorary degrees to men of outstanding accomplishments. It is most effective when rendered by a male quartet or chorus, either in unison or in parts, a capella or with instrumental accompaniment, but can also be sung by a women's or a mixed chorus.

The chorus number of *Gaude Mater Polonia* may be obtained in the following versions: for men's chorus, for women's chorus and for mixed chorus, at 10 cents per copy. From:

> Boosey, Hawkes, Belwin, Inc.
> 43 West 23rd Street
> New York, N. Y.

The same versions may also be obtained from corresponding houses in the following countries:

In England . . . . . . 295 Regent Street
London, W. 1

In Canada . . . . . . 10 Shuter Street
Toronto

In Australia . . . . . . National Building
250 Pitt Street
Sydney

In Africa . . . . African Book and Music Dept.
Commerce Chambers
84 Loop Street
Capetown, S. A.

(4) Address on Nicholas Copernicus. This can be prepared by a local or invited astronomer, mathematician, physicist or anyone interested in the history of civilization in general and in this subject in particular. In a good many cases the information on Copernicus given in this brochure may be sufficient to serve as basis for a popular address, with such additional reading as may be done in local libraries. We are sorry, however, that it would be impossible for the Kosciuszko Foundation to supply speakers.

(5) Short Pageant: The Initiation of Copernicus into the University of Krakow.

We are all familiar with our contemporary student antics in connection with initiation into college fraternities and sororities. The practice is "as old as the hills." There is nothing new that the Polish students at Krakow in the days of Copernicus did not know, or did not put in practice. Only there the initiation of the "greenhorns" at that time was not into any particular fraternity, but into the brotherhood of university scholars in general.

By way of entertainment and especial attraction, those schools, colleges and universities that have dramatic departments may want to prepare a ten or fifteen minute pageant depicting this Polish medieval university custom. Authentic university costumes of both students and tutors are herein reproduced as suggestions for costume designs. Considerable freedom of interpretation may be exercised in the conception and execution of such a pageant.

(6) The Death of Copernicus, and the Birth of Modern Science.

These Copernican programs are intended partly as a commemoration of the death of Copernicus, but mostly as a celebration of the birth of modern science. It would therefore be most fitting, if circumstances warrant, to pay tribute to other scientists who, together with Copernicus, pioneered the way to modern science.

(7) The Universality of Modern Science.

Copernicus wrote his great work in Latin. Just as Latin was a universal language which all scholars of his day knew and used, science also is universal. It recognizes no political boundaries, pays no attention to nationalities. All contributions became common property of all men. Whether it be Nicholas Copernicus and Marie Sklodowska Curie the Poles, Leonardo da Vinci and Galileo Galilei the Italians, Francis Bacon and William Harvey the Englishmen, Walter Reed and Thomas A. Edison the Americans, Jean Baptiste Lamarck and Louis Pasteur the Frenchmen, Tycho Brahe the Dane, Shibasaburo Kitasato the Japanese, Johann Kepler the German, and Albert Einstein the German Jew—they all belong in the same fraternity of servants and benefactors of mankind. And when the work of destruction is over, that of healing and reconstruction will begin and science (not Polish, Italian, English, Japanese, French, Danish, Jewish or American science, but simply science) will again become the handmaid of civilization.

This spirit of unity and universality of science could most appropriately be emphasized as a part of the tribute to Copernicus.

(9) *Copernicana* Exhibits. Yale University, in conjunction with the Copernican program, is planning to arrange an exhibit of all items in possession of the Yale Library pertaining to Copernicus. The New York Public Library will have a similar exhibit — under the title: "Copernicus and His Contemporaries." A number of other institutions and larger libraries, private and public, will arrange *Copernicana* Exhibits.

Since almost every larger library has something on Coper-

nicus or astronomy, either books or pictures, it is suggested
that some exhibits be planned—however modest—for the week
commencing Monday, May 24, 1943; or, if this date be incon-
venient, arrange them at an earlier or later date.

THE COPERNICAN QUADRICENTENNIAL NATIONAL COMMITTEE

As this brochure goes to press, a National Committee under
the above name is being organized with extensive plans for
a national celebration in New York, Monday evening, May 24,
1943. A large representation of foreign scholars from many
lands is also expected. As the plans crystallize they will be
announced through the press.

It is hoped that the proceedings of the main celebration
will be published in an appropriate volume or album, which
will also list all the institutional and local Copernican
Quadricentennial celebrations, tributes, etc., so as to give this
important anniversary a permanent record. It is therefore
most desirable that every Copernican program, however modest, be reported to the Kosciuszko Foundation so that we can
make the record as complete as possible.

(Above) "The Broken Note" Signal of the "Trumpeter
of Krakow."
No. 1 on the Program.

(Below) Gaude Mater Polonia.
No. 3 on the Program.

Gau _ de Ma.ter Po.lo _ _ _ _ ni _ a,

Pro _ le fe _ cun _ da no _ bi _ _ li,

Sum.mi re.gis ma _ gna _ li _ _ _ a,

Lau _ de fre.quen.ta vi _ _ _ gi _ _ _ _ li.

POLISH NATIONAL ANTHEM

English version by
Edwin Markham

Melody - Oginski

From the Botsford collection of Folk Songs. Copyright 1922 and 1931 by G. Schirmer, Inc. Printed by permission of the publisher and Mrs. Botsford.

Po - land shall a - gain be - free, vic - to - ry is

near - ing. vic - to - ry is near - ing.

Jeszcze Polska nie zginęła

Jeszcze Polska nie zginęła,
Kiedy my żyjemy;
Co nam obca przemoc wzięta,
Mocą odbierzemy.
    Marsz, marsz, Dąbrowski,
    Z ziemi włoskiej do polskiej.
    Za twoim przewodem,
    Złączym się z narodem.

Choć sąsiady nas zniszczyły,
I broń nam zabrały,
Sparty piersi murem były
I te nam zostały.
    Marsz, marsz, Dąbrowski,
    Z ziemi włoskiej do polskiej,
    Każdy z nas chęć czuje,
    Wodza nie brakuje.

Dzielność wolnego oręża,
Starzec opowiada,
Aby szukać tego męża
Młody na koń siada.
    Marsz, marsz, Dąbrowski,
    Z ziemi włoskiej do polskiej,
    Wolność, dawne hasło
    Jeszcze w nas nie zgasło.

Polish National Anthem

Poland's glory is not vanished
While her sons remain.
And her flag that once was banished
Shall return again.

Refrain
March, march, Dombrowski!
Hark the people come with cheering,
Poland shall again be free, victory is nearing.

Poland's wrongs shall all be righted,
Youth of Poland call.
Freedom's torch we bring uplighted,
Spartan breasts our wall.

Refrain – March, march etc.

Poland's sons again will muster,
And drive out the foe;
Will bring back her ancient lustre,
Bring her joy for woe.

Refrain – March, march etc.

English version by
Edwin Markham

Plate I

[76]

How Polish Students Dressed
in the Student Days of Copernicus (1491-95)

In those days universities were in the service of the church. Professors were generally churchmen; and students, for the most part, were preparing themselves for the church. Hence, they all dressed modestly and their costumes resembled those of priests and monks. Sombre colors—black, dark blue and gray —predominated (see Plate I on p. 76).

But, as in our own days, there were rich and poor students, the serious and the frivolous. Copernicus undoubtedly belonged in the serious group. Although modest (long and sombre dress) was prescribed for all, the rich and the frivolous were often guilty of breach of discipline. Already in the last decade of the XV century there was at the University of Krakow a rebellion against the traditional dress. Such boys as were full of "college spirit" began to wear "indecent" (vestis indecens) clothes: short, tight-fitting and hilariously gaudy (see Plate II on p. 78).

Plate II shows a violent reaction against the prescribed dress, under the influence of Italian universities from which Polish students were returning in increasing numbers. All sorts of brilliant color combinations began to appear, such as: navy and sapphire-blue, yellow, red, cherry-red, even slippers were red or blue. Each student tried to exercise his ingenuity by having a different color combination from the rest. Fourth from left, for example, is the dandy, with puffed sleeves and striped (light-blue and black) breeches. A typical color combination may be in number one: sapphire-blue jacket, yellow sleeves, cherry-red velvet sleeve cuffs, cherry-red beret with gray feather, cherry-red slippers with gray fur trimmings. In other cases colors were differently combined.

When it came to initiation of "greenhorns" (only they were called beani—"yellow beaks"*) and to hazing, the frivolous perhaps dominated the scene.*

Plate II

[78]

Part IV

IN THE NAME OF COPERNICUS

Is Poland to Be a "Cultural Wilderness"?

O N THE OCCASION of the Copernican Quadricentennial, the Kosciuszko Foundation will commence its preliminary and preparatory work looking forward towards the post-war educational reconstruction of Poland. Thus the commemoration of a great Polish scientist of the distant past may become a call to the living to pass on a torch of light to those of the future.

When the Germans came to Poland in 1939, those *Kultur-traeger* ("carriers of culture") announced that they would make a "cultural wilderness" — *ein Kulturwueste* — out of the land they conquered. And they are doing it with relentless efficiency. All the universities and all secondary schools, with the exception of some trade schools, have been closed. The reason given: "A slave nation needs no higher education" and can therefore dispense with such luxury. Scientific laboratories, museums and university libraries have been looted; hundreds of university professors have been thrown into concentration camps; scores of them died in these camps, scores of others died after release and before the firing squad. Of the 200 members of various Faculties of the University of Krakow alone, the Alma Mater of Copernicus, twenty-nine are definitely know to be dead—fourteen in the concentration camp.

The University of Copernicus, including its Department

of Astronomy, suffered the most. Towards the end of October, 1939, the occupational authorities informed the Rector of the university to open the university as usual and to call all faculty members for this ceremony, the special feature of which was to be a lecture by a German scientist on the policy of National Socialism towards universities. When in the morning of November 6th they all assembled in the university hall, which is graced by the original painting of Copernicus by the national painter of Poland, Jan Matejko, the Gestapo surrounded the building and a Dr. Meyer of the Gestapo appeared on the lecture platform with the following announcement: "As you all understand German, it will not be necessary for me to have my address translated into the Polish. Because you tried to open the university without our knowledge and consent, because you carried on your laboratory work and conducted examinations without our approval, and, finally, because this university of yours has always been a bastion of what you call Polish culture,—you are all under arrest." Then the doors flung open, 170 members of the faculty (including professors emeriti, some old and feeble) were thrown into lorries and carried off to unknown destination. Within a few weeks urns with ashes began to arrive; early in February, 1940, 105 living skeletons arrived in Krakow—many of whom did not linger long—and the rest are still paying for the crime of having been connected with that "bastion of what the Poles call Polish culture."

History will pass its judgment and the mills of gods in due time will grind out their own measure of justice.

In the meanwhile, it would be comforting to those Polish scholars and scientists who are still alive to know that, on the occasion of the Copernican Quadricentennial, we have decided to help them or their successors in the rebuilding of their workshops that have been destroyed or despoiled.

Best American Books as Nucleus

Even while this second World War is still raging and nobody knows when it is going to end, governments, institutions and individuals are already making plans for the post-war period of reconstruction. Complete blueprints with all details could not be drawn now, yet certain problems are already apparent and plans can be made ahead of time looking forward to their solution.

Four things are certain:

1. That there will be a United States of America, playing a leading role in the future scheme of things and in intercontinental affairs.

2. That such Poles as shall have survived, whether professors or students, teachers or pupils, will try under new conditions—whatever they may be—to reorganize their teaching facilities and to teach or prepare themselves for such tasks of construction and reconstruction as they will be facing in the future.

3. That the new Poland will have to start from scratch so far as higher educational facilities in general are concerned, and libraries in particular. Most university buildings are still standing, and it is hoped that they will be standing, but they have been despoiled of equipment and libraries have been looted. Such book collections as have not been destroyed will be disgorged and in time will be restored to Poland; but in the meanwhile, professors and students of the restored New Poland will need basic books, especially such as will contain progress made in America during the period when Polish science and learning were blacked out, so that they can start their work immediately.

4. That the scholars of the New Poland will be looking to America for such help in this respect as may be possible for us to give them.

[81]

One of the best services we can render on behalf of America to the reconstruction of higher education in Poland will be along lines of helping the Polish higher institutions of learning to establish nuclei of their working libraries with basic books published in America in various fields. A collection of from 5,000 to 10,000 well chosen titles, with several duplicates of each volume making a total of from 20,000 to 30,000 volumes, would fill the basic initial needs. Some volumes may be secured as donations from individual American scholars, from library duplicates and from publishers; others will be purchased as funds become available and actual conditions call for the final step in the program now undertaken.

The Kosciuszko Foundation has already received enthusiastic expressions of personal interest and assurances of moral support and cooperation of officials of the American Library Association, the Library of Congress and of other institutional representatives to whom the educational needs of the Poland of Tomorrow were incidentally mentioned.

Definite preparatory steps will be taken on the occasion of the Copernican Quadricentennial. As the first token of our future intentions and the practical expression of our good will, the Kosciuszko Foundation is making arrangements to send on this occasion to the Polish Medical Faculty at Edinburgh, Scotland, some of our best medical books and a number of the leading medical journals, published in America. With the definite understanding, however, that after the war these and other books and journals, which may subsequently be shipped, will be transferred to medical schools in Poland.

The preliminary or preparatory work, to which reference was made above, will consist of preparing master indices of the best works in every essential field published in America; where, when, and by whom published; where available when actually needed, and at what price if any.

Two Chairs in American Civilization

As a part of the quadricentennial tribute to Copernicus the Board of Trustees of the Kosciuszko Foundation, at their annual meeting on October 9, 1942, besides approving the above plan, passed a resolution expressing their intention to establish and support, with the cooperation of their friends old and new, two Chairs in American Civilization; one at the University of Krakow, the Alma Mater of Copernicus, and the other in the leading university of the nation's capital.

Filled periodically by American scholars who are recognized authorities in their respective subjects, each Chair will cover such basic fields as American history, constitutional development and political institutions (i.e. democracy in theory and practice), American contributions in the fields of business organization, science, industry and technology; also certain aspects of American culture as expressed in art, architecture, music and literature. The nature of the American nation *(E Pluribus Unum)*, with especial emphasis on the Polish immigration to the United States, the geographic and occupational distribution of the present Americans of Polish descent or extraction, their contributions to America, their characteristics (good and bad) as revealed under the impact of new conditions—should be included among the subjects to be taught or lectured on within the regular curriculum of each of the proposed two Chairs.

Each Chair will have its own collection of books, a Seminar Library of say 5,000 titles, including the best books the United States has produced on its own civilization and the leading scholarly journals. Whether these books are directly donated or purchased from funds donated, each book will have a specially designed *Ex Libris* with the name and address of the donor of the book or of funds for the purchase thereof, so that the future generations of students will always know through whose generosity a given book was made possible. This *Ex Libris* will apply also to books mentioned before, in other fields than American civilization.

It is hoped that in the Poland of Tomorrow there will be a re-orientation towards and even closer economic, political and cultural relationships with the Anglo-Saxon countries; that English will be taught in all secondary schools, if not as a required foreign language at least with first preference out of two or three; that all future scholars of Poland will be reading new American books and will be as fully informed of American progress in science and other lines of endeavor as they have been informed hereto of progress made by some of the continental nations whose languages they knew.

It would be pretentious if not preposterous to claim that everything America has produced is the best, that American institutions can be bodily transplanted into other social and spiritual climates, or that from American experience in every sphere of activity all nations can draw uniform benefits. It would be equally pretentious even to suggest to other nations that they must draw all applicable lessons from American experience in order to be happy, prosperous and progressive. However, those willing to learn can learn a great deal from America that they can adapt to their own conditions, from which they can profit greatly and which will facilitate better understanding of and therefore closer relations with America.

We have in America now over fifty Polish refugee scholars, who occupied academic positions in Poland ranging from senior assistant to full professor, including a few deans and rectors. They are learning English, and they are learning a great deal besides English. Most of them will go back and start where they left off. No, they cannot exactly start where they left off; first they will have to help rebuild and reorganize. Who knows, but the old national systems of education may become as obsolete as the Ptolemaic system in astronomy; and some new system of education may have to be organized, around some central idea or form of international organiztion in relationship to which each national system will be revolving like a planet in the Copernican heliocentric conception! Washington may be that center, or near-center, but let us not press the analogy any further. The fact is that the impact of *American* "ideology" will be tremendous in more ways than one.

There are at least twice as many Polish refugee scholars in England as there are in America. And they, in turn, will bring with them the English version of Anglo-Saxon ideology. Again, in England, there are in the Polish Army thousands of young men with substantial intellectual background — many with interrupted university education—who will form educational cadres and intellectual leadership for the Poland of Tomorrow.

In view of the deliberate destruction by the invader of Polish intellectual capital, so as to achieve a "cultural wilderness," it seems almost inevitable that America — the United States of America—may have to "lend-lease" to Poland thousands of its teachers, professors, doctors, priests, business organizers, nurses and dietitians, builders and architects, until a new generation of Poles is raised and educated to take their places. In a good many professions, where knowledge of the Polish language is indispensable, these will have to be recruited from the ranks of Americans of Polish descent or extraction.

All these factors and considerations seem to indicate that the absorption of American contributions, of American ideas and ideals, into the life-blood of the Poland of Tomorrow, will not be as slow as has been the acceptance of the Copernican system of the universe.

[85]

THE KOSCIUSZKO FOUNDATION
What Is It?   What Is It For?

ESTABLISHED IN 1925 as a living memorial to General Tadeusz Kosciuszko, the Polish national patriot and American Revolutionary War hero, the Foundation's main objective has been to promote the exchange of students and professors between Poland and the United States and to cultivate cultural and intellectual relationships between these two countries.

From the time it was organized, this Foundation has "exchanged" between Poland and America 169 students, research scholars and professors (101 Americans to Poland and 68 Poles to the United States); has granted $122,009.97 in scholarships without drawing upon its capital funds; has been instrumental in the publication of a number of books on cultural topics pertaining to both countries, and upon demand has furnished informational service in thousands of cases.

In this catastrophe that befell the Western Civilization in general and Poland's national life and cultural achievements in particular, the main objective of the Foundation has been to help preserve the brains of Poland by helping Polish scholars to survive—and when the war is over, to help in the educational reconstruction of Poland. Since 1939 the Foundation has directly aided materially and otherwise in the bringing of twelve Polish university professors to America, rendered assistance in a good many other cases of Polish intellectuals of non-academic standing and has extended material aid, whenever direct contacts were possible, to over 200 Polish refugee professors and scholars in distress scattered in several countries and continents. About 10 percent of the total number of Polish professors and instructors as of pre-war days received aid from the Foundation. No money was or is being sent to occupied territories. Over $50,000 has been secured and spent so far since the fall of 1939 for aid of Polish refugee students and professors.

As to the Foundation's interest in the Copernican Quadricentennial celebrations—it is a part of its general interest in the promotion of intellectual and cultural relations between Poland and the United States.

The *Board of Trustees* are: WILLIS H. BOOTH, ERIC P. KELLY, HENRY NOBLE MACCRACKEN, STEPHEN P. MIZWA, PAUL MONROE, EDWARD C. SMITH, JOHN B. STETSON, M. S. SZYMCZAK, THOMAS J. WATSON, M. F. WEGRZYNEK.

The *Officers* are: HENRY NOBLE MACCRACKEN, President; M. F. WEGRZYNEK, Vice-President; EDWARD C. SMITH, Treasurer, City Bank Farmers Trust Company; STEPHEN P. MIZWA, Secretary and Executive Director.

VARIOUS AVAILABLE EDITIONS

This little book, "Nicholas Copernicus, 1543-1943," has been published in various editions and bindings:

1. Popular edition, pamphlet-bound, at 75¢ per copy. For schools, on orders of 20 or more copies, at 50¢ per copy.

2. Library edition, bound in cloth, at $1.50 per copy.

3. Subscription edition, limited to eight hundred copies and serially numbered, bound in boards of "Riviera Rose" color, at $2.50 per copy.

Of this edition the first five hundred copies have been autographed by the artist of the colorful frontispiece portrait of Copernicus and by the author. These copies are being presented to each of the first five hundred friends of the Kosciuszko Foundation contributing $5.00 or more.

✦ ✦ ✦

A limited number of copies of the same colorful drawing of Copernicus which appears as frontispiece has been printed (in five colors) from the original master plates on extra heavy paper with wide margins and suitable for framing, and these prints are available at $1.00 per print.

THE KOSCIUSZKO FOUNDATION
149 East 67th Street
New York, N. Y.

6 + C 7 9 ° 5 M